S0-AAB-594

RAINBOW WRITING

By
Mary Euretig
and
Darlene Kreisberg

Text format and design • **Maureen Shanahan**
Cover design and illustration • **Lisa Bacchini Graphic Design and Illustration**

DREAM
TREE
PRESS

To creative children everywhere
- especially Andrew, Matthew, Kristen, Michelle, Allison, Nicole and Michael

Special thanks to the students and faculty
at Saint Mary's Hall in San Antonio, Texas
who encouraged us
and served as the writing laboratory for this book.

Copyright ©1990 by Mary Euretig

All rights reserved, including the right
to reproduce this book or portions thereof
in any form.

Published by
DREAM TREE PRESS
3836 Thornwood Dr.
Sacramento, CA 95821

ISBN 0-9628216-0-8

Additional copies of *Rainbow Writing* are available by contacting:
DREAM TREE PRESS
3836 Thornwood Dr., Sacramento, CA 95821

First Edition

Printed in the United States of America

All rights reserved. No part of this work covered by the copyright hereon may be reproduced or used in any form or by any means - graphic, electronic, or mechanical, including photocopying, recording, taping, or information storage and retrieval systems - without written permission of the publisher.

Dear Parents,

Young children love to write. As teachers, we have seen this love of writing demonstrated repeatedly. In schools with strong writing programs, most people are amazed at the quality of children's writing and the enthusiasm with which they approach the task. This book grew out of our commitment to develop writing ability in children.

Writing improves with practice. One of the goals of an early writing program is to develop fluency, that is, the ability to expand on a topic and to write with ease. Beginning writers often need guidance in choosing and developing ideas for writing. Our book offers this type of guidance.

Each month, <u>Rainbow Writing</u> introduces the child to a new theme, one that focuses on the child's own experiences and everyday life. Beginning with a calendar page, your child will fill in the number grid then answer basic questions about each month. This is followed by activities such as making lists, surveying friends, recording data on a chart, as well as open-ended writing suggestions and frames for drawing pictures. Research questions are also included and may need your assistance. Individual expression of ideas is encouraged through the blank pages at the end of each month where the child is free to write on a self-selected topic. The activities are designed to promote creative expression and logical thinking, both of which must be nurtured for full writing potential to develop.

Beginning writers can and will write about things that are important to them, but only if you avoid pointing out or correcting spelling errors. Doing so will inhibit the amount and sophistication of writing that children will attempt. Skill in spelling develops gradually over many years, but young writers should not have to wait to write until they can spell. In fact, the best way to improve spelling is through frequent writing and reading. Ask your child to read his writing aloud and watch the pride and enthusiasm that is reflected in voice and face. The best response you can offer is genuine interest in your child's work.

As your child enjoys completing the activities in this book, you will notice an increase in both your child's interest in writing and in the ability to write. In addition, you will have a treasured keepsake of a very special time in your child's life.

Mary Euretig

Darlene Kreisberg

Dear Friends,

Welcome to <u>Rainbow</u> <u>Writing</u>. This is a very special book because YOU will be writing and drawing in it.

Each month you will find:

    ** a calendar with:

        * numbers to fill in and

        * activities to complete

    ** ideas for you to write about

    ** frames for you to draw pictures

    ** questions for you to ask your family and friends

You will also find blank pages in each month. These pages are for you to write whatever you would like! You can write about something special that happened to you that month. You might want to invent a new food or create an animal. You could write about your friends or your pets or anything else you can think of. Don't forget to add some pictures.

Have fun with your book. Keep it in a special place and share it with your friends and family.

Happy writing!

                    Your friends,

                    The Rainbow Writers

1991

JANUARY
S	M	T	W	T	F	S
		1	2	3	4	5
6	7	8	9	10	11	12
13	14	15	16	17	18	19
20	21	22	23	24	25	26
27	28	29	30	31		

FEBRUARY
S	M	T	W	T	F	S
					1	2
3	4	5	6	7	8	9
10	11	12	13	14	15	16
17	18	19	20	21	22	23
24	25	26	27	28		

MARCH
S	M	T	W	T	F	S
					1	2
3	4	5	6	7	8	9
10	11	12	13	14	15	16
17	18	19	20	21	22	23
24	25	26	27	28	29	30
31						

APRIL
S	M	T	W	T	F	S
	1	2	3	4	5	6
7	8	9	10	11	12	13
14	15	16	17	18	19	20
21	22	23	24	25	26	27
28	29	30				

MAY
S	M	T	W	T	F	S
			1	2	3	4
5	6	7	8	9	10	11
12	13	14	15	16	17	18
19	20	21	22	23	24	25
26	27	28	29	30	31	

JUNE
S	M	T	W	T	F	S
						1
2	3	4	5	6	7	8
9	10	11	12	13	14	15
16	17	18	19	20	21	22
23	24	25	26	27	28	29
30						

JULY
S	M	T	W	T	F	S
	1	2	3	4	5	6
7	8	9	10	11	12	13
14	15	16	17	18	19	20
21	22	23	24	25	26	27
28	29	30	31			

AUGUST
S	M	T	W	T	F	S
				1	2	3
4	5	6	7	8	9	10
11	12	13	14	15	16	17
18	19	20	21	22	23	24
25	26	27	28	29	30	31

SEPTEMBER
S	M	T	W	T	F	S
1	2	3	4	5	6	7
8	9	10	11	12	13	14
15	16	17	18	19	20	21
22	23	24	25	26	27	28
29	30					

OCTOBER
S	M	T	W	T	F	S
		1	2	3	4	5
6	7	8	9	10	11	12
13	14	15	16	17	18	19
20	21	22	23	24	25	26
27	28	29	30	31		

NOVEMBER
S	M	T	W	T	F	S
					1	2
3	4	5	6	7	8	9
10	11	12	13	14	15	16
17	18	19	20	21	22	23
24	25	26	27	28	29	30

DECEMBER
S	M	T	W	T	F	S
1	2	3	4	5	6	7
8	9	10	11	12	13	14
15	16	17	18	19	20	21
22	23	24	25	26	27	28
29	30	31				

1992

JANUARY
S	M	T	W	T	F	S
			1	2	3	4
5	6	7	8	9	10	11
12	13	14	15	16	17	18
19	20	21	22	23	24	25
26	27	28	29	30	31	

FEBRUARY
S	M	T	W	T	F	S
						1
2	3	4	5	6	7	8
9	10	11	12	13	14	15
16	17	18	19	20	21	22
23	24	25	26	27	28	29

MARCH
S	M	T	W	T	F	S
1	2	3	4	5	6	7
8	9	10	11	12	13	14
15	16	17	18	19	20	21
22	23	24	25	26	27	28
29	30	31				

APRIL
S	M	T	W	T	F	S
			1	2	3	4
5	6	7	8	9	10	11
12	13	14	15	16	17	18
19	20	21	22	23	24	25
26	27	28	29	30		

MAY
S	M	T	W	T	F	S
					1	2
3	4	5	6	7	8	9
10	11	12	13	14	15	16
17	18	19	20	21	22	23
24	25	26	27	28	29	30
31						

JUNE
S	M	T	W	T	F	S
	1	2	3	4	5	6
7	8	9	10	11	12	13
14	15	16	17	18	19	20
21	22	23	24	25	26	27
28	29	30				

JULY
S	M	T	W	T	F	S
			1	2	3	4
5	6	7	8	9	10	11
12	13	14	15	16	17	18
19	20	21	22	23	24	25
26	27	28	29	30	31	

AUGUST
S	M	T	W	T	F	S
						1
2	3	4	5	6	7	8
9	10	11	12	13	14	15
16	17	18	19	20	21	22
23	24	25	26	27	28	29
30	31					

SEPTEMBER
S	M	T	W	T	F	S
		1	2	3	4	5
6	7	8	9	10	11	12
13	14	15	16	17	18	19
20	21	22	23	24	25	26
27	28	29	30			

OCTOBER
S	M	T	W	T	F	S
				1	2	3
4	5	6	7	8	9	10
11	12	13	14	15	16	17
18	19	20	21	22	23	24
25	26	27	28	29	30	31

NOVEMBER
S	M	T	W	T	F	S
1	2	3	4	5	6	7
8	9	10	11	12	13	14
15	16	17	18	19	20	21
22	23	24	25	26	27	28
29	30					

DECEMBER
S	M	T	W	T	F	S
		1	2	3	4	5
6	7	8	9	10	11	12
13	14	15	16	17	18	19
20	21	22	23	24	25	26
27	28	29	30	31		

JANUARY

January 199_

Sunday	Monday	Tuesday	Wednesday	Thursday	Friday	Saturday

Fill in the missing days for January.

January 10th is on a _____.
(day)

There are ____ Wednesday's this month.

The holidays this month are New Year's

Day on January ____ and Martin Luther
(date)

King's birthday on January ____.
(date)

Someone I know with a birthday this

month is _____.

January is the first month of the new year.

The brand new year is _____.

I will turn ____ years old this year.

Some things I hope will happen this year are:

1.

2.

3.

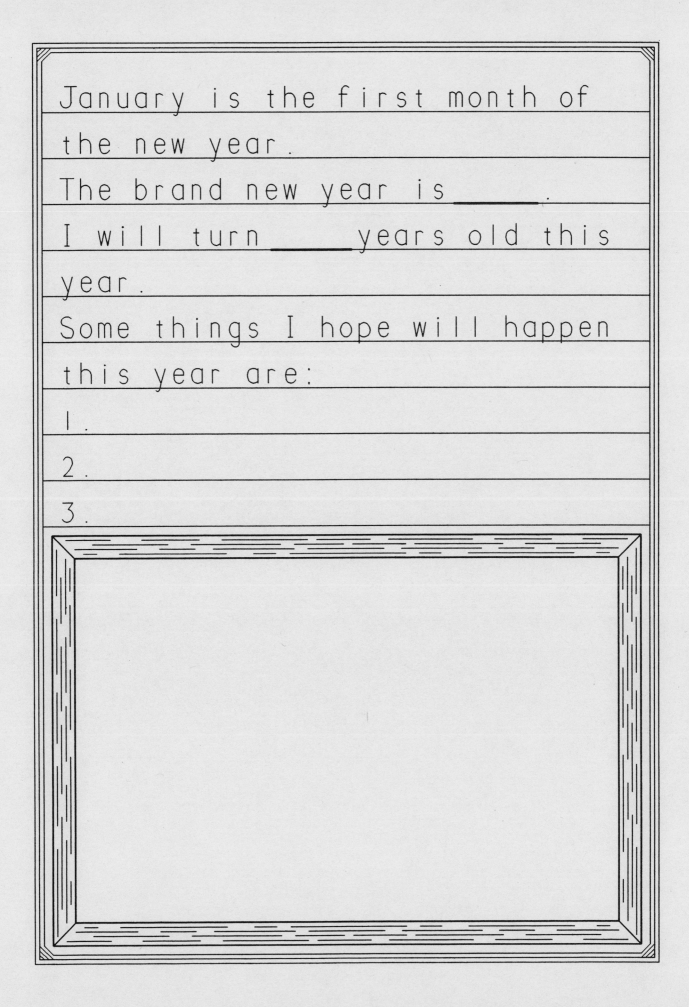

Here is a list of things I can
do well.

1.

2.

3.

4.

Other people I know can do things
well, too.

My mother is good at _____

_____.

My father is good at _____

_____.

My friend _____ is good at

_____.

Here is a list of things I wish
I could do.

1.

2.

3.

Here is a story about something
new or special that happened to
me this month.

The best surprise this month was

_____ .

A person who made me happy this

month was _____ because

_____

_____ .

_____ made me angry

because _____

_____ .

One new book or story I read this

month was _____ .

Something new I learned this month

was _____ .

I think my parents were proud of

me when _____

_____ .

Next month I'd like to try _____

_____

_____ .

FEBRUARY

❤ February 199_ ❤

Sunday	Monday	Tuesday	Wednesday	Thursday	Friday	Saturday

There are _____ days in February.

February 19th is on a _____.
(day)

There are _____ Sundays this month.

Valentine's day is on February _____.
(date)

February _____ is President's Day.
(date)

People I know with birthdays in

February are _____

_____.

February is the month of
friendship.　These are some of
my friends.

This is what I like about my
friends.

Whenever I have a fight with one
of my friends, I feel _____

_____.

If I had a fight with one of my
friends and wanted to make up
this is what I would do.

_____

_____

_____

_____

_____

Here is a list of things I enjoy
doing with my friends.

1. _____

_____

2. _____

_____

3. _____

_____

This is a picture of a card I would like to give my friend on Valentine's Day.

Here is how I celebrated Valentine's Day.

The best surprise this month was

_____.

A person who made me happy this

month was _____ because

_____

_____.

_____ made me angry

because _____

_____.

One new book or story I read this

month was _____.

Something new I learned this month

was _____.

I think my parents were proud of

me when _____

_____.

Next month I'd like to try _____

_____.

MARCH

March 199_

Sunday	Monday	Tuesday	Wednesday	Thursday	Friday	Saturday

Fill in the missing days for March.

There are _____ days in March.

March 3rd is on a _____.
(day)

There are _____ Fridays this month.

St. Patrick's day is on March _____.
(date)

March _____ marks the first day of Spring.
(date)

People I know with birthdays this month

are _____.

March is the month of leprechauns and
wishes. If I could make three wishes,
I would wish for these things.

1.

2.

3.

This is a picture of one of my wishes.

I asked three of my friends to tell
me what they would wish for if they
had one wish. This is what they said.

_____ wishes for _____
(name)
_____ wishes for _____
(name)
_____ wishes for _____
(name)

Leprechauns like to play tricks on
people and sometimes get into
trouble. I got into trouble one time
for

_____

_____

_____ .

One sunny day in March I made friends
with a leprechaun. His name was

_____ . I'll tell you what he
looked like.

_____

_____ .

My leprechaun friend and I played together all day and had lots of adventures. This is a story about my favorite one.

The best surprise this month was

_____ .

A person who made me happy this

month was _____ because

_____

_____ .

_____ made me angry

because _____

_____ .

One new book or story I read this

month was _____ .

Something new I learned this month

was _____ .

I think my parents were proud of

me when _____

_____ .

Next month I'd like to try _____

_____

_____ .

APRIL

April 199_

Sunday	Monday	Tuesday	Wednesday	Thursday	Friday	Saturday

Fill in the missing days for April.

There are _____ days in April.

In April there are _____ Mondays.

Easter is on April _____.
(date)

April _____ is Passover.
(date)

People I know with birthdays this

month are _____

_____

Pets are fun.

(If you don't have a real pet, write about a pretend one.)

I have a pet. My pet is a _____.

My pet's name is _____.

Here is what my pet looks like.

Here is a list of words to describe

my pet.

_____

_____

My pet is as big as _____.

as funny as _____.

as cute as _____.

My pet loves to eat _____ .

My pet sleeps on _____ .

These are the things I do to take

care of my pet.

1. _____

2. _____

3. _____

Today I watched my pet for 10 minutes.
Here are some of the things my pet did.

The funniest thing my pet does is:

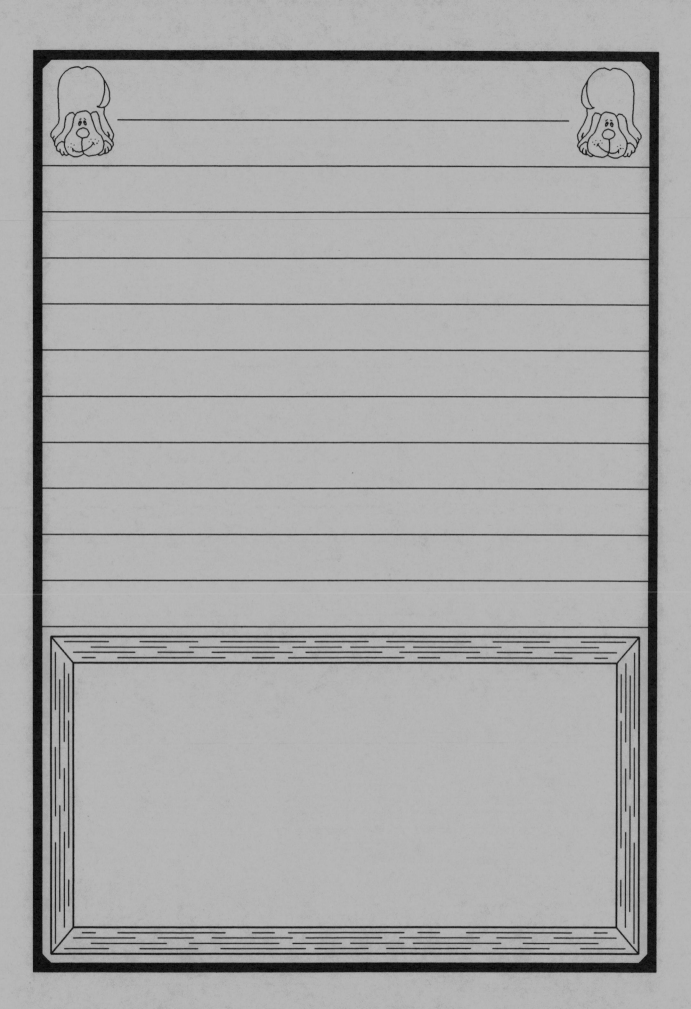

The best surprise this month was

_____ .

A person who made me happy this

month was _____ because

_____

_____ .

_____ made me angry

because _____

_____ .

One new book or story I read this

month was _____ .

Something new I learned this month

was _____ .

I think my parents were proud of

me when _____

_____ .

Next month I'd like to try _____

_____

_____

_____ .

MAY

May 199_

Sunday	Monday	Tuesday	Wednesday	Thursday	Friday	Saturday

Fill in the missing days for May.

May 24th is on a _____.
                              (day)

There are ___ Fridays this month.

May Day is on May ___.   Mother's Day
                    (date)

is celebrated on May ___.
                      (date)

Memorial Day falls on May ___.
                           (date)

People I know with birthdays this

month are _____.

My name is _____ and I am part of
a family. These are the other people
in my family.

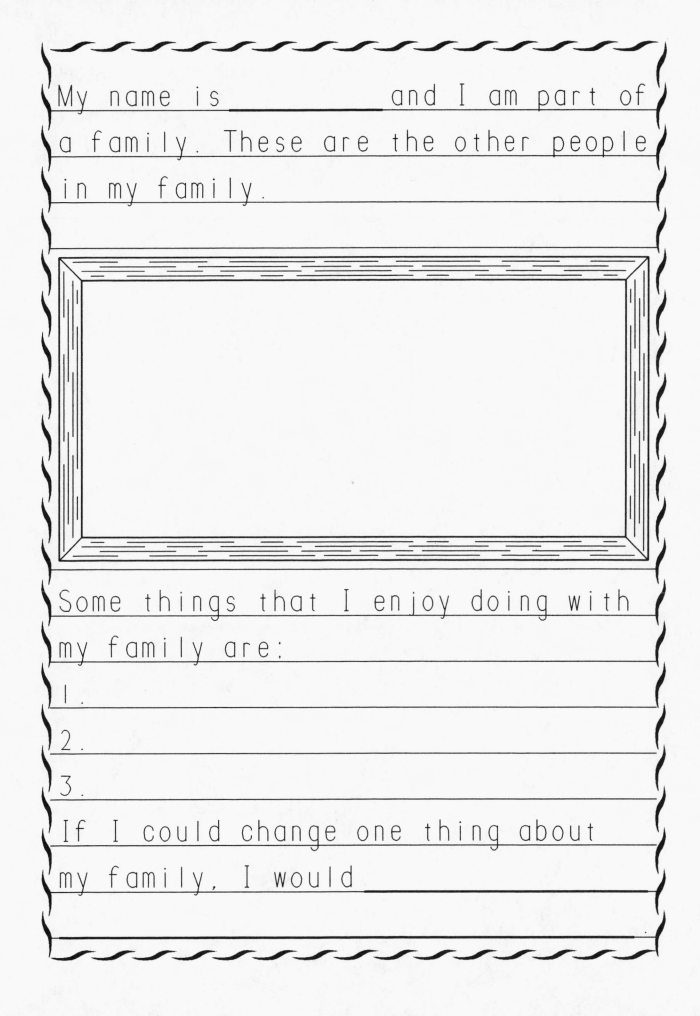

Some things that I enjoy doing with
my family are:

1.

2.

3.

If I could change one thing about

my family, I would _____

Ask eight friends how many people are in their family. For each friend, find the number they tell you on the chart. Color in a square above that number.

2	3	4	5	6	7

Number of People in Family

My family has rules. These are three of the rules.

1.

2.

3.

There is one more rule I wish we had and that is _____

Mother's Day is coming soon. This is
a picture of a card I would like to
make for my mother.

On the inside of this card I would
write _____

_____.

This is what makes my family special.

_____

_____

_____

The best surprise this month was

_____ .

A person who made me happy this

month was _____ because

_____

_____ .

_____ made me angry

because _____

_____ .

One new book or story I read this

month was _____ .

Something new I learned this month

was _____ .

I think my parents were proud of

me when _____

_____ .

Next month I'd like to try _____

_____

_____ .

JUNE

June 199_

Sunday	Monday	Tuesday	Wednesday	Thursday	Friday	Saturday

Fill in the missing days for June.

There are _____ days in June.

June 10th is on a _____.
(day)

There are _____ Wednesdays this month.

The last day of school is June _____.
(date)

People I know with birthdays this

month are _____

_____.

It's June and school is out! I
learned lots of new things this year.
Some of the things I learned are:

1.

2.

3.

One thing I'll really miss about
school is _____

_____.

Something I won't miss is _____

_____.

In my free time this summer, I want to

1.

2.

3.

One thing I would like to do this
summer that I have never done before is

_____ .

Ask three friends what they will be
doing this summer. Write what they
said on the chart.

Friend	Summer Activity
1.	
2.	
3.	

If I could take a trip anywhere in the
world this summer, I would go to

_____

_____

_____ .

The people I would like to take with me are:

1.

2.

3.

Here are the things I need to pack for my trip

The best surprise this month was

_____ .

A person who made me happy this

month was _____ because

_____

_____ .

_____ made me angry

because _____

_____ .

One new book or story I read this

month was _____ .

Something new I learned this month

was _____ .

I think my parents were proud of

me when _____

_____ .

Next month I'd like to try _____

_____

_____ .

JULY

July 199_

Sunday	Monday	Tuesday	Wednesday	Thursday	Friday	Saturday

Fill in the missing days for July.

There are _____ days this month.

July 11th is on a _____.
                        (day)

There are _____ Fridays in July.

Independence day is celebrated on

July _____.   People I know with
        (date)

birthdays this month are _____

_____.

It's fun to go outdoors in July.

When I go outside, I like to _____

_____

_____ .

Here are three things I see when I

go outside.

1. _____

2. _____

3. _____

I love it when the weather is _____

_____ .

Thunderstorms make me feel _____

_____ .

Sometimes the thunder is as loud as

_____ .

When it rains hard, sometimes I

think _____

_____

_____ .

Sit outside for five minutes. Close your eyes. Listen to the sounds around you. How many different sounds do you hear? Write down some of the sounds you heard.

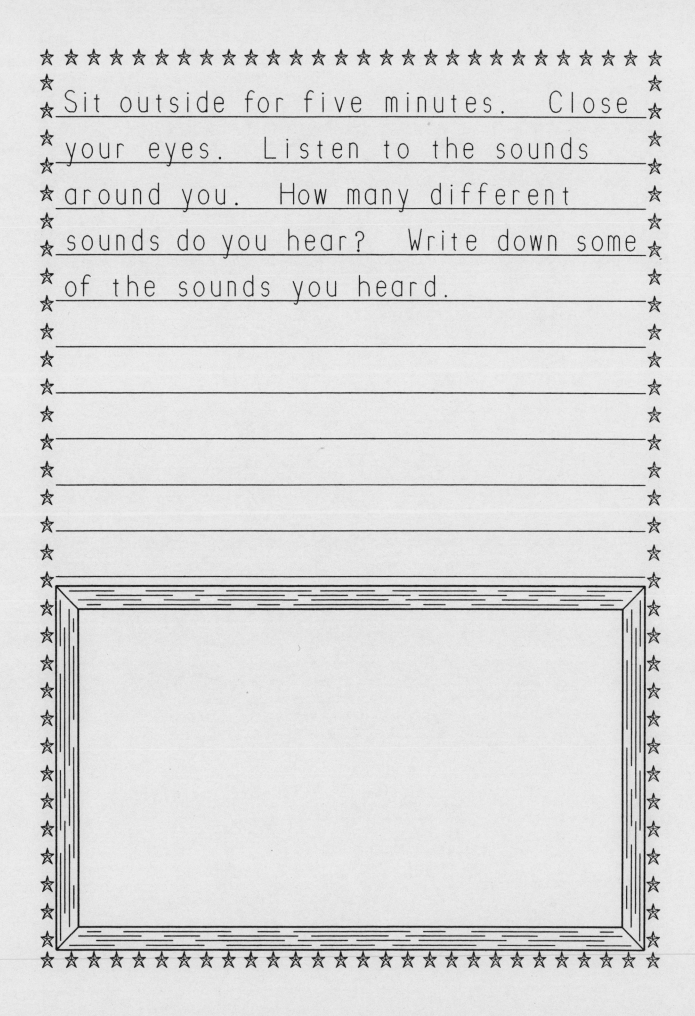

Lots of animals live outdoors in the woods. My favorite outdoor animal is _____. If I were an outdoor animal, here are three things I might eat.

1. _____

2. _____

3. _____

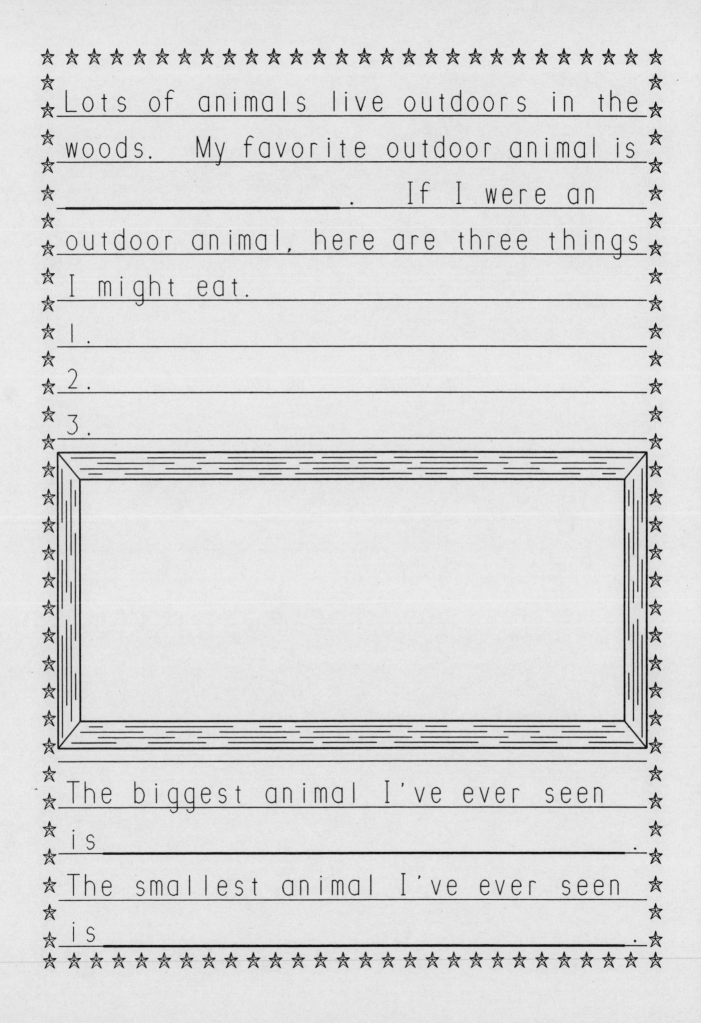

The biggest animal I've ever seen is _____.

The smallest animal I've ever seen is _____.

★ ★

The best surprise this month was

_____.

A person who made me happy this

month was _____ because

_____

_____

_____ made me angry

because _____

_____.

One new book or story I read this

month was _____.

Something new I learned this month

was _____.

I think my parents were proud of

me when _____

_____.

Next month I'd like to try _____

_____

_____.

★ ★

AUGUST

August 199_

Sunday	Monday	Tuesday	Wednesday	Thursday	Friday	Saturday

Fill in the missing days for August.

There are _____ days in this month.

August 2nd is on a _____.
(day)

There are _____ Mondays in August.

August 31st is on a _____.
(day)

There are _____ Saturdays this month.
(date)

People I know with birthdays this

month are _____.

August is a good month for
daydreaming. My favorite place to
daydream is_____.
I like to sit back and think about
_____.

Sometimes I like to imagine I am

_____

_____

_____

_____.

Here is one place you should never
daydream_____.

Pick a day when the sky is full of clouds. Lie down in your backyard or any comfortable, safe place outdoors. Watch the clouds for five minutes. How many clouds did you see _____?

The clouds looked like _____

_____

_____.

They made me think of _____

_____.

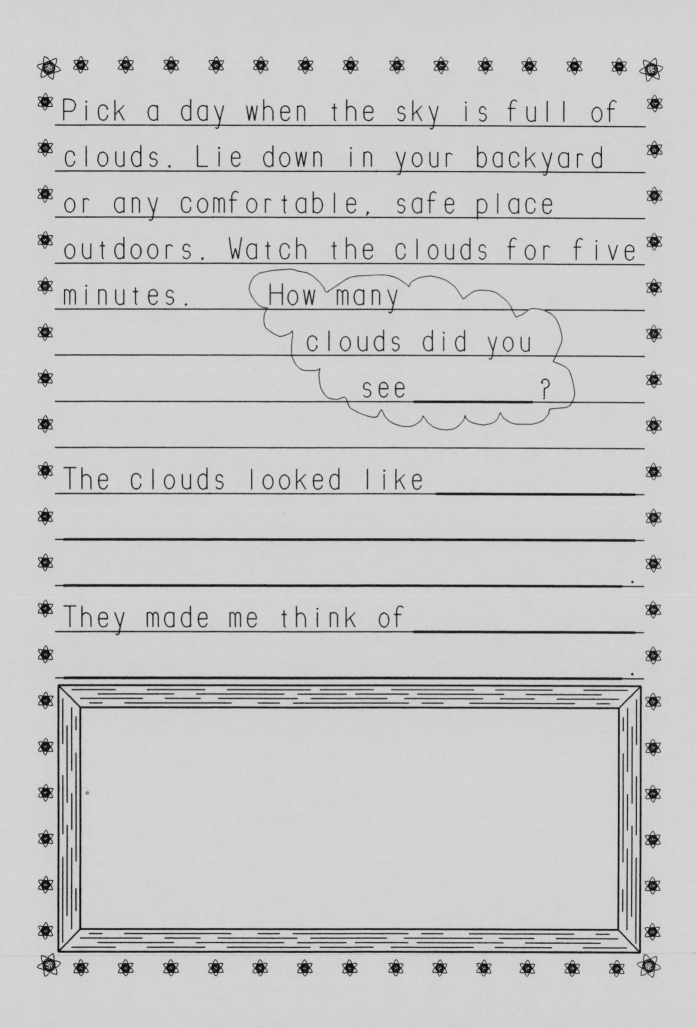

In my dreams, I can be anything!

3 things I would like to be are:

1. _____

2. _____

3. _____

If I could be an animal, I would be
a _____ and here's what I
would do: _____

_____

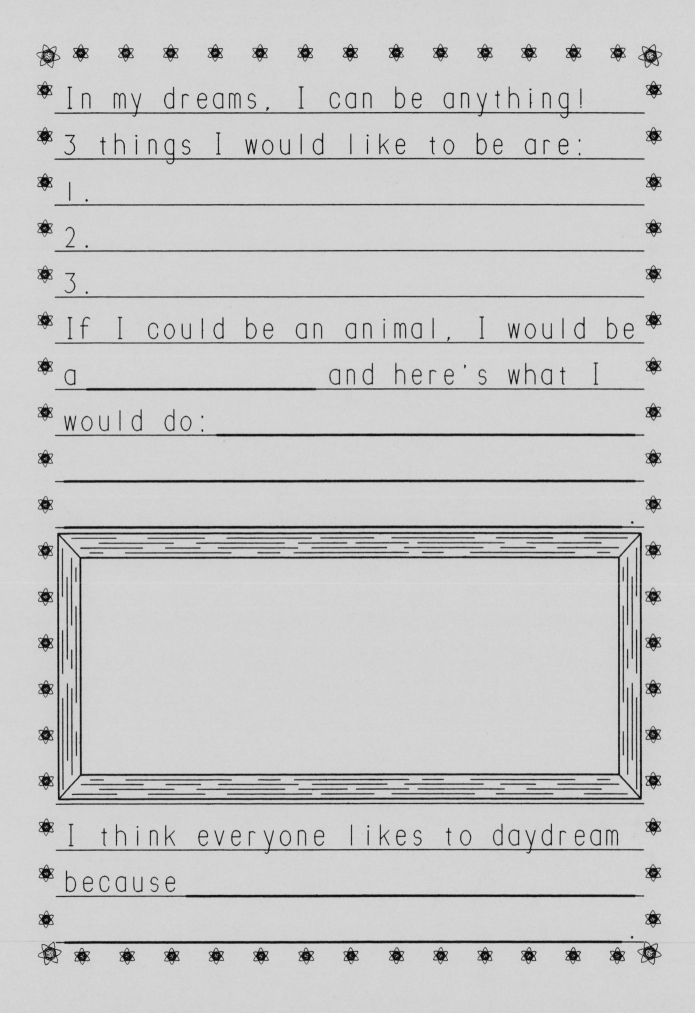

I think everyone likes to daydream
because _____

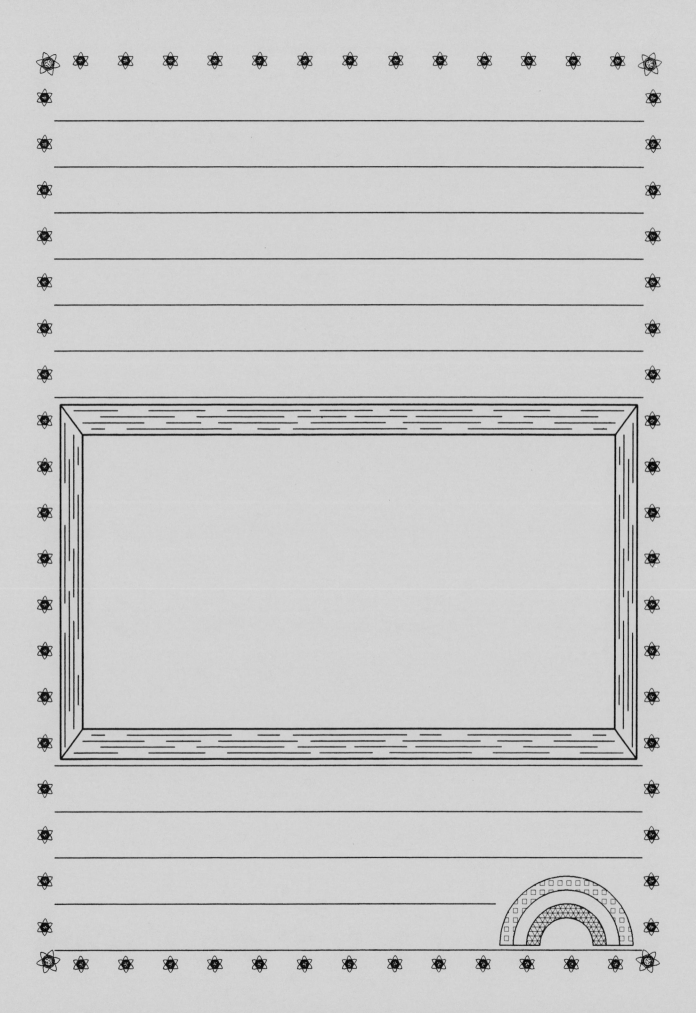

The best surprise this month was
_____.

A person who made me happy this
month was _____ because
_____
_____.

_____ made me angry
because _____
_____.

One new book or story I read this
month was _____.

Something new I learned this month
was _____.

I think my parents were proud of
me when _____
_____.

Next month I'd like to try _____
_____
_____.

SEPTEMBER

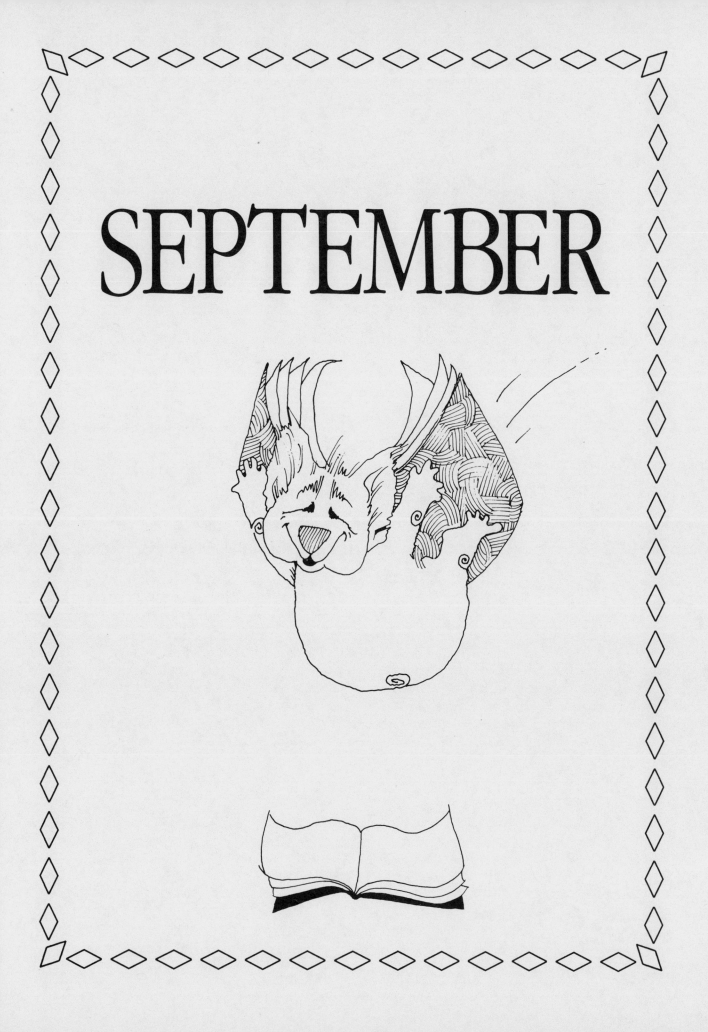

September 199_

Sunday	Monday	Tuesday	Wednesday	Thursday	Friday	Saturday

There are _____ days in September.

September 12th is on _____.
(day)

There are _____ Sundays this month.

Labor Day is on September _____.
(date)

September _____ is the first day of
(date)
school. People I know with birthdays

this month are _____

This is the start of a new school year. I am in ___ grade. My teacher is _____. I like him or her because _____

_____.

There are ___ students in my class. The day before school started I felt

_____.

Three things I hope to learn about in in school this year are:

1. _____

2. _____

3. _____

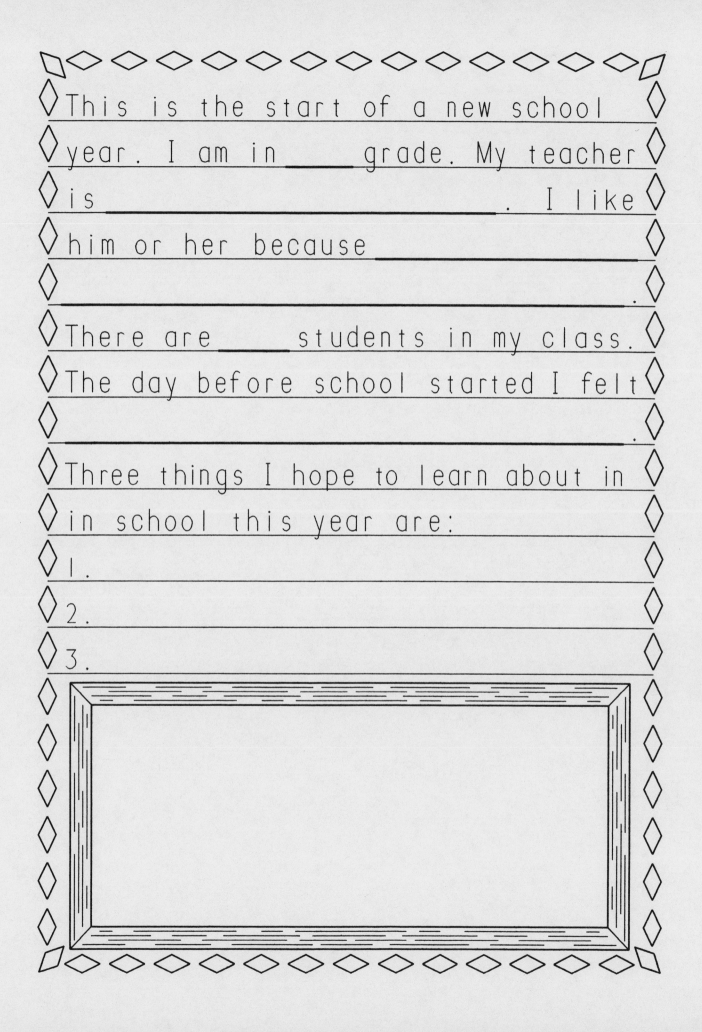

I watched the children playing on the playground for five minutes. These are some of the things they were doing.

1.

2.

3.

4.

My favorite subject is _____.

I like it best because _____

I asked three friends to tell me
their favorite subject.   This
is what I found out.
_____ likes _____
    (name)   (subject)
_____ likes _____
    (name)   (subject)
_____ likes _____
    (name)   (subject)

If I were a teacher I would _____
_____
_____.

If I were the principal I would
_____
_____.

When I grow up I would like to be
a _____.

I would like to invent something
which would _____.

By the end of the year I should be
able to _____.

The best surprise this month was

_____ .

A person who made me happy this

month was _____ because

_____

_____ .

_____ made me angry

because _____

_____ .

One new book or story I read this

month was _____ .

Something new I learned this month

was _____ .

I think my parents were proud of

me when _____

_____ .

Next month I'd like to try _____

_____

_____

OCTOBER

October 199_

Sunday	Monday	Tuesday	Wednesday	Thursday	Friday	Saturday

Fill in the missing days for October.

October 5th is on a _____.
(day)

There are ____ Tuesdays this month.

In October there are ____ days.

Halloween is celebrated on October

____. People I know with birthdays
(date)

this month are _____

_____.

Books are special. My favorite time
to read is _____. My favorite
place to read is _____.

My three favorite books are:

1. _____

   by _____

2. _____

   by _____

3. _____

   by _____

I asked three friends what books they liked. Here is what they said.

Friend	Favorite Book
1.	
2.	
3.	

If I could be a character in a book, I would like to be _____ from the book _____.

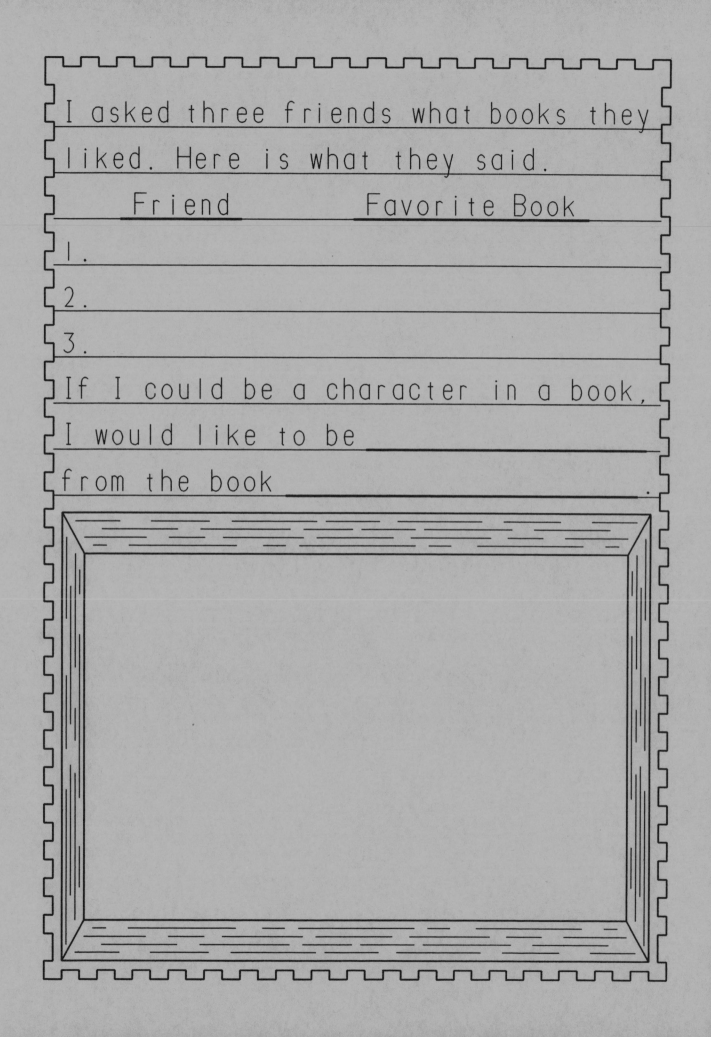

The best thing about reading books
is _____

_____ .

The worst thing about reading books
is _____

_____ .

When I was little my favorite story
was _____ .

I think writers should write more
about _____ .

Here is a list of things I would
write about.

1. _____

_____

2. _____

_____

3. _____

_____

_____

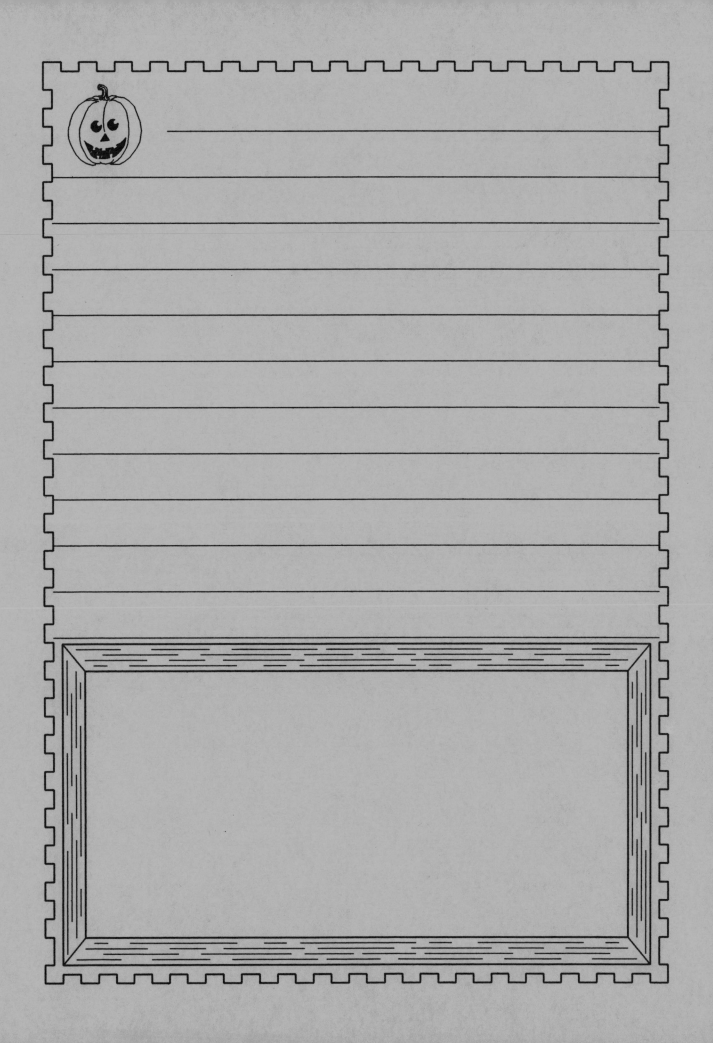

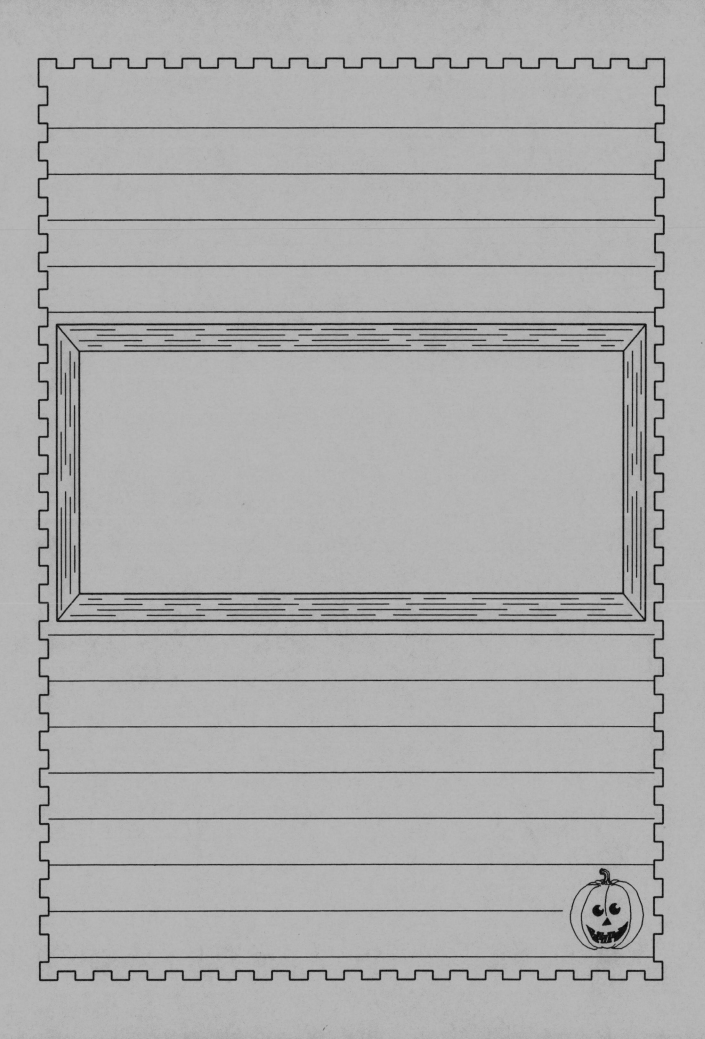

The best surprise this month was

_____ .

A person who made me happy this

month was _____ because

_____

_____ .

_____ made me angry

because _____

_____ .

One new book or story I read this

month was _____ .

Something new I learned this month

was _____ .

I think my parents were proud of

me when _____

_____ .

Next month I'd like to try _____

_____

_____ .

NOVEMBER

November 199_

Sunday	Monday	Tuesday	Wednesday	Thursday	Friday	Saturday

Fill in the missing days for November.

There are _____ Mondays this month.

November 6th is on a _____.
                          (day)

We celebrate Veteran's Day on

November _____ and Thanksgiving Day
            (date)

on November _____.
                (date)

People I know with birthdays this

month are _____.

November is a time for giving thanks.
Here is list of things I am most
thankful for.

1. _____
2. _____
3. _____
4. _____

My family celebrates Thanksgiving by

_____

_____ .

This is what our Thanksgiving dinner
looks like.

My favorite food on the table is ____

_____ .

I asked three friends to tell me their favorite food.

Friend	Favorite Food
1.	likes
2.	likes
3.	likes

If I could plan the menu for dinner, this is what I would serve.

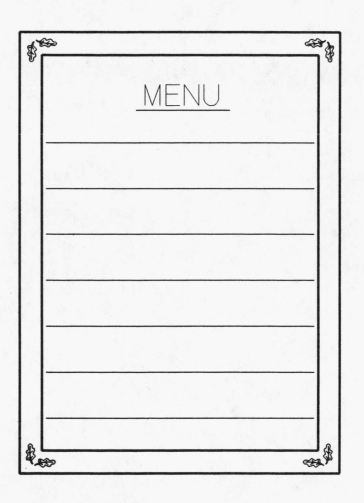

MENU

_____

_____

_____

_____

_____

_____

_____

I think I would have enjoyed
celebrating the first Thanksgiving
with the pilgrims and Indians
because _____

_____

One thing that might not have been
fun is _____

_____

Here is a story about the pilgrims,
Indians and me.

_____

_____

_____

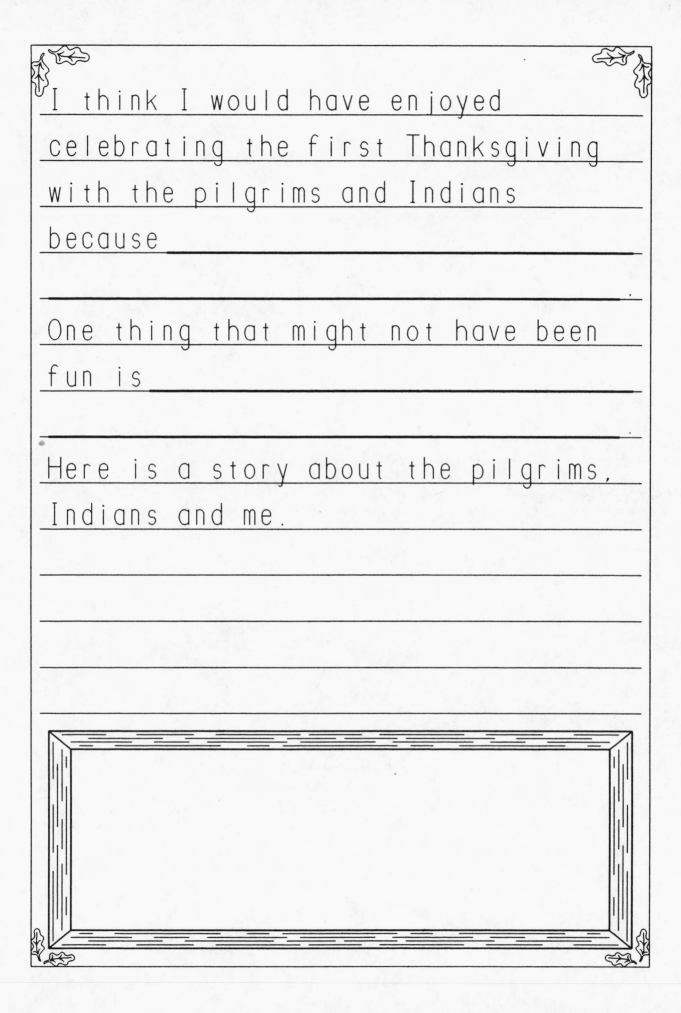

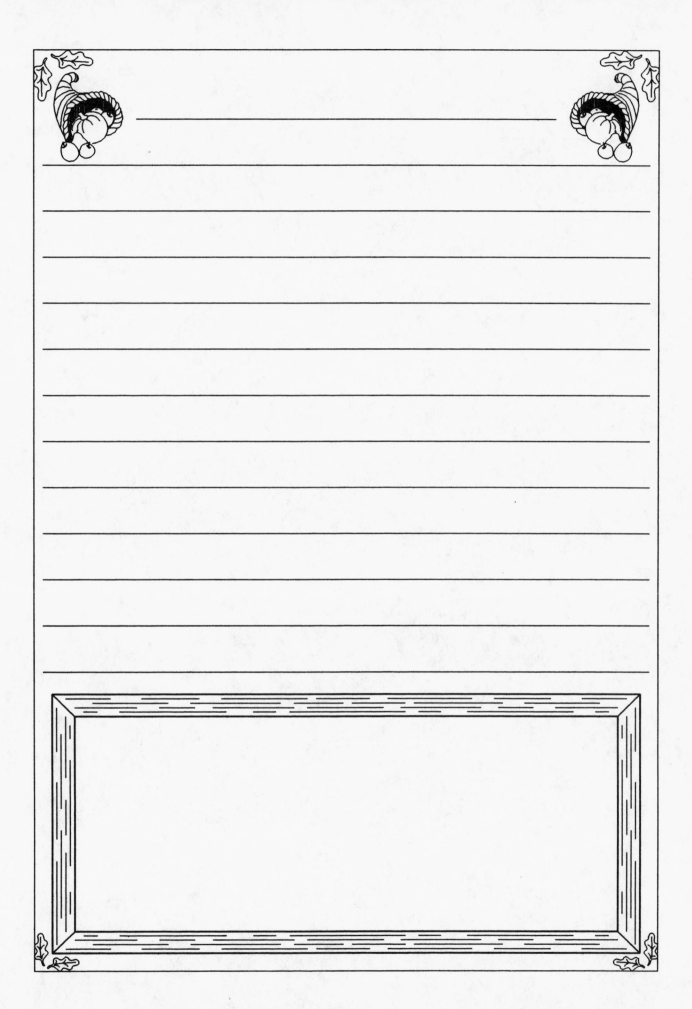

The best surprise this month was
_____ .

A person who made me happy this
month was _____ because
_____
_____ .

_____ made me angry
because _____
_____ .

One new book or story I read this
month was _____ .

Something new I learned this month
was _____ .

I think my parents were proud of
me when _____
_____ .

Next month I'd like to try _____
_____
_____ .

DECEMBER

December 199_

Sunday	Monday	Tuesday	Wednesday	Thursday	Friday	Saturday

Fill in the missing days for December.

December 19th is on _____.
(day)

There are ____ Thursdays this month.

Christmas Day is celebrated on the

_____.
(date)

Hannukah begins on the _____.
(date)

People I know with birthdays this

month are _____.

December is the month for
celebrations! My favorite holiday
this month is _____.
Things that make this holiday
special are:
1. _____
2. _____
3. _____
4. _____

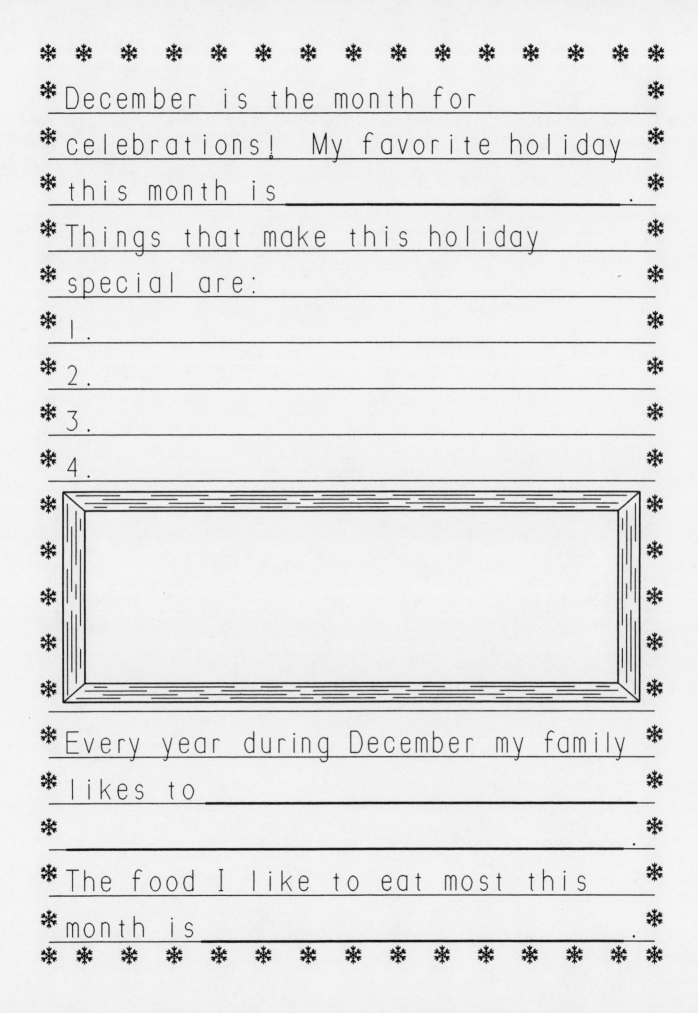

Every year during December my family
likes to _____
_____.
The food I like to eat most this
month is _____.

If I could invent a holiday, it
would be called _____.
This is a picture of what people
would do on my holiday.

Here is a story about my holiday.

_____

_____

_____

_____

_____

Birthdays are very special. My

birthday is_____.

Ask ten friends what their birth

month is. For each friend, find the

month they tell you on the chart.

Color a square above that month.

Jan	Feb	Mar	Apr	May	Jun	Jul	Aug	Sep	Oct	Nov	Dec

This is what I found out. The month

with the most birthdays is_____.

No one had a birthday in_____.

There were_____ birthdays in June.

On my next birthday I would like to

_____.

✳ ✳ ✳ ✳ ✳ ✳ ✳ ✳ ✳ ✳ ✳ ✳ ✳ ✳

✳The best surprise this month was _____

✳ _____ .

✳A person who made me happy this

✳month was _____ because

✳ _____

✳ _____ .

✳ _____ made me angry

✳because _____

✳ _____ .

✳One new book or story I read this

✳month was _____ .

✳Something new I learned this month

✳was _____ .

✳I think my parents were proud of

✳me when _____

✳ _____

✳Next month I'd like to try _____

✳ _____

✳ _____

✳ ✳ ✳ ✳ ✳ ✳ ✳ ✳ ✳ ✳ ✳ ✳ ✳ ✳